FREE COURSE
WITH
BOOK PURCHASE

Email: Team@ProcurementQueen.com with the subject "My Free Gift"

DAILY AFFIRMATION

$ I am winning contracts.

$ I am persistent.

$ I am helpful.

$ I enjoy learning.

$ I am manifesting my goals.

$ I am a good decision-maker.

$ I am successful.

THANK YOU

I want to thank **GOD** for answering my prayers and for blessing me. I thank God for everything that has happened in my life.

I want to thank my children, **Sterlyn and Phoenix Williams**, for their support. When they were babies, I read them procurement books for bedtime stories, and together we learned about this new industry. My kids are my cheerleaders. Sterlyn and Phoenix, I love you so much.

I want to thank my biological dad, Clement Williams. May his soul rest in peace .

I want to thank the people that were instrumental in providing me with the opportunity to enter the procurement industry. Thank you for believing in me,

thank you for supporting me.

Thank you to **Catherine Wilson**, the president of the United Way of Greater Newark, for believing in me and for providing the opportunity for me to teach procurement courses to the community.

THANK YOU TO EVERYONE THAT SUPPORTS ME.

TO: _____

Thank you for your support and the purchase of this book. Denise "Procurement Queen ™ " Williams' core value is the economic empowerment of entrepreneurs. Denise has over eighteen years of experience leading Procurement Teams in various industries with an annual spend of over $2B. In Chess, The Queen's focus is guarding the Board against strikes, which could result in losses. As your Firm's Queen, Denise will improve supplier experience, streamline operations, and revitalize stale processes. Denise grew the supplier diversity programs, trained vendors and internal personnel.

Support Minority and Women businesses

The Capability Statements found in this book are from real companies. Please reach out to those businesses to purchase goods and services. Follow them on social media, like, tag and share.

Moore Business Success, LLC

A woman-owned boutique consulting firm that specializes in assisting small businesses, entrepreneurs, and start-up technology firms navigate through business compliance, contract formation, human resources benefits management and legal strategic planning.
info@Moorebusinesssuccess.com

Miller Resource Group

Miller Resource Group provides a comprehensive coaching program supporting athletes who are entering/re-entering the corporate workforce.
www.millerresource.net
info@millerresource.net

Moore Business Success, LLC
CAPABILITES STATEMENT

Moore Business Success, LLC is a woman-owned boutique consulting firm that specializes in assisting small businesses, entrepreneurs, and start-up technology firms navigate through business compliance, contract formation, human resources benefits management and legal strategic planning. We are collaborative and team-oriented, driven to leave clients more informed, empowered, compliant, and successful than we found them. For Moore Assistance, contact us at info@moorebusinesssuccess.com

CORE COMPETENCIES

- Business Entity Formation and Dissolution
- Real Estate Purchase Agreements
- Governing Contract Creation
- Independent Contractor Agreements
- Human Resources Management
- Intellectual Property Security
- Employee Benefits Agreements
- Legal Strategic Planning
- Continuing Education Instructor
- Succession Planning

DIFFERENTIATORS

- Seasoned Professional
- Sr. Compliance Investigator
- Negotiated millions in RE
- Former litigator
- 20+ Years Adjunct Professor

CERTIFICATIONS

Juris Doctorate (1998)

L.LM Taxation (2006)

Retirement Benefits Associate Cert.

Group Benefits Advisor Cert.

MWBE- Certification (New Jersey)

NAIC CODES

91840 - EE Benefits Consulting Services
92400 - Educational/Training Services
91874 - Legal Consulting
92416 - Course Development Services

Your success is our business

Miller Resource Group
GROUP

The Athletes Career Coach
Established 2018

CAPABILITY STATEMENT
Human Resources for Athletes| Career Coaching | Leadership | Education
www.millerresource.net   Dallas/Fort Worth, TX   info@millerresource.net

Miller Resource Group provides a comprehensive coaching program supporting athletes who are entering/re-entering the corporate workforce. Our clients are equipped to identify the right career fit and achieve success in the hiring process. We use proven, effective HR strategies for clients to launch their careers.

As a Minority Owned, Woman Owned Small Business we are committed to applying sound HR practices that bring athletes immediate solutions.

- Job and Career Fit
- Customized Career Strategies
- Job Market Analysis
- Resume Support
- Interview Preparation
- Executive Coaching
- Leadership Training
- Salary Negotiation

NAIS CODES:
541612 - Human Resources Consulting Services

541618 - Other Management Consulting Services

611710 - Educational Support Services

SIC CODES:
8742 - Management Consulting Services

9441 - Administration of Social and Human Resource

Achievements and Qualifications
- 15+ years executive HR leadership for Fortune 500 companies
- Diverse experience with HR Management across a variety of workgroups and industries
- Multi-Site HR management experience across various geographies and global locations
- Certified Executive Coach
- Certified Hogan Assessment Coach
- Masters of Business Administration - Strategic Leadership

Procurement Queen is a registered trademark of Denise Williams. Published by Learn Now Grow, LLC Printed in the United States Copyright © 2021 by Denise Williams ISBN 978-1-7359634-0-2. All Rights Reserved.

Author: Denise Williams is available for speaking engagements, workshops, partnerships. Please email inquiries to Team@procurementqueen.com
Paperback ISBN: 978-1-7359634-0-2
Library of Congress Number: 2021905350
Printed in the United States of America
First Printing: 2021

This book may be purchased for educational, business, or sales promotional use. Denise is available for speaking engagements, workshops, partnerships, etc. For more information, please email inquiries to Team@procurementqueen.com

Facebook: ProcurementQueen

Instagram: ProcurementQueen

www.ProcurementQueenAcademy.com

WWW.ProcurementQueen.com

Disclaimer

The Publisher has strived to be accurate and complete as possible in the creation of this report, notwithstanding the fact that she does not warrant or represent at any time that the contents within are accurate due to the rapidly changing nature of the Internet.

While all attempts have been made to verify information provided in this publication, the Publisher assumes no responsibility for errors, omissions, or contrary interpretation of the subject matter herein. Any perceived slights of specific persons, people, or organizations are unintentional.

In practical advice books, like anything else in life, there are no guarantees of income made. Readers are cautioned to rely on their own judgement about their individual circumstances to act accordingly. This book is not intended for use as a source of legal, business, accounting or financial advice. All readers are advised to seek services of competent professionals in legal, business, accounting and finances fields.

DIY
PROCUREMENT QUEEN SERIES

CAPABILITY STATEMENT

Written by:

Denise Williams, MBA, MS, CPSD, CPSM, QPA, RPPO, CIPS Diploma level

"The Procurement Queen® "

HOW TO USE THIS WORKBOOK

This workbook contains a step-by-step guide on how to create your capability statement. The capability statement will set you apart from competitors. You may be the only vendor at a bid opening or pre-bid conference to provide the buyer or contracting agent a capability statement. The capability statement is largely used in the government contract (public) sector and can be used to market your company services to private corporations too. To me, it is a win, win and is a low-cost marketing tool. This book is dedicated to business owners who want to understand how to compete for contracts. I want you to follow the steps I provide, and when you win your first contract, please share it with me. I feel so vibrant when I create the tools to help you compete, win, and perform. My intention is for you to succeed. I want to empower you, and when you succeed, I want you to be a blessing to someone else. What I know for sure is that you have the power to design the life you want to live. I challenge you to try the action, steps, and strategies. I want to share information that outlives me. Every business owner should have a Capability Statement for their business.

Announcement: On Monday, January 18, 2021, I launched the 5 Day Capability Statement challenge visit www.procurementqueenacademy.com to join.

When you create the Capability Statement, please tag "Procurement Queen" in the post. @ProcurementQueen #ProcurementQueen

I want you to read the daily affirmation. Control the thoughts that are in your head.

- » **I am winning contracts**; whether your contract is $250 or $10 million, it is still a contract.

- » **I am persistent** your breakthrough is around the corner, so keep moving forward.

- » **I am helpful**; when you read this book, you are learning valuable information that you can share with someone else.

- » **I enjoy learning**, the regulations change, and I want you to educate yourself continuously. You got this.

Denise hopes that this book helps small business owners and aspiring entrepreneurs better navigate the government and private contracting process. Denise wants you to compete, win, and perform.

Daily Affirmation

$ I am winning contracts.

$ I am persistent.

$ I am helpful.

$ I enjoy learning.

$ I am manifesting my goals.

$ I am a good decision-maker.

$ I am successful.

$ I am _____

$ I am _____

$ _____

$ _____

$ _____

$ _____

$ _____

$ _____

$ _____

MEET THE AUTHOR

DENISE WILLIAMS

"The Procurement Queen"

Denise "The Procurement Queen" Williams is America's favorite procurement educator. Denise helps small business owners and aspiring entrepreneurs better navigate the government and private contracting process via the delivery of courses that includes seminars, workshops, curricula, and training. Her seminars are engaging, and she provides her clients with valuable information to compete for contracts.

Denise has over eighteen years of experience and held positions of increasing levels of responsibility, having started as a Financial Analyst and Senior Financial Analyst, before being promoted to Assistant Director of Purchasing at the largest school district in New Jersey with a budget of $990M. As the Assistant Director of Purchasing, she was responsible for overseeing the Procurement, Strategic Sourcing, eProcurement functions and managed a team of strategic sourcing analyst. Areas of spend activity include the purchase of Professional Services, Equipment and Supplies, Contracted Services, and other operational supplies to support the Districts' educational goals.

Denise earned a Bachelor's Degree in Finance from Rutgers University and a Master's in Business Administration and Accountancy from Saint Peter's University. She is a Qualified Purchasing Agent (QPA) for the state of New Jersey, Registered Public Purchasing Official (RPPO), and hold a Diploma certification from the Chartered Institute of Procurement (CIPS), Certified Professional in Supply Management (CPSM), and Certified Professional in Supplier Diversity (CPSD). Denise remains an active member of the Institute for Supply Management (ISM). Denise lives in New Jersey, and she enjoys spending her time with her daughter Sterlyn and son Phoenix.

An exclusive interview with Denise Williams

Question and Answers interview

1. *Question: So Denise, please tell me what is Procurement?*

   Answer: Procurement is the acquisition of goods or services. Let me make it relatable for you, I am a single mom of two kids, and I practice procurement when I need to purchase a cleaning service; you know that's the service for a company to clean your house. I am not a super mom, I need help. I purchased legal services when I was going through a divorce.

   Let us talk about goods. I often enjoy drinking coffee in the morning. The cups that I use to drink my coffee are considered goods, the creamers are goods, the coffee pods are goods. A few other examples of goods are animal food, chairs, balloons, paper, and shoes. All the services and goods I mentioned are also purchased by the government. The government buys coffee, chairs, paper, and janitorial cleaning services. There are a lot of contracting opportunities for you.

2. *Question: Denise, I noticed you have an accent; please share your background?*

   Answer: I was born in the beautiful country of Dominica. Dominica is well known for its rainforest and natural hot springs. I grew up with my mother and father. At the age of 9, my mom and I came to America, the land of opportunity; my dad had a successful business and career and did not want to give that up to start over in America. I remember speaking to my dad over the phone.

3. *Question: Where did you go to school?*

   We lived in Irvington, New Jersey, for several years, where I attended Chancellor Ave Public School, then we moved to Newark, New Jersey, and I attended Vailsburg Middle School and Bloomfield Tech High School. We later moved to Union, New Jersey, and I attended Union High School. I later graduated from Union County College, Rutgers University, and Saint Peters University.

4. *What fuels your passion for wanting to help business owners successfully compete for private and government contracts?*

   Answer: When I hear the pains, struggles, and loss of hope from business owners, it bothers my soul. When I serve, whether it is through teaching, donating, or sharing a smile, it fuels my soul. Minorities and women businesses have been left out of the procurement process, and I want to provide the tools they need to succeed.

5. *How did you get involved in Procurement?*

Answer: I was a tenured teacher and taught high school students physics and business courses. During summer break, I saw a job opening for Assistant Director of Purchasing and decided to apply without any procurement experience because it sounded interesting and the salary was higher. After the interview, I was offered the job. Everyone thought I was crazy to give up a tenured teaching position for a job with no union protection. I have positive beliefs about myself, I love myself, and I can take anything that happens to me. I can also turn it around and win. I am grateful to the selection committee for providing me with the opportunity to lead and start a career in procurement.

Table of Contents

WIN # 1

READ YOUR DAILY AFFIRMATION

AFFIRMATION

$ I am winning contracts.

$ I am persistent.

$ I am helpful.

$ I enjoy learning.

$ I am manifesting my goals.

$ I am a good decision-maker.

$ I am successful.

$ _____

$ _____

$ _____

$ _____

$ _____

$ _____

$ _____

$ _____

$ _____

My Notes

WIN # 2

CAPABILITY STATEMENT

Procurement Queen Tip: Congratulations on taking the step to create your company capability statement. The capability statement provides potential clients and contractors a snapshot of how great your company is. Yes, your capability statement should include the core competencies such as what does your company do really well, how is your company different from your competitors, what certifications does your company have, and who have you worked with in the past. Think of it as a 1-page document where you brag about your company. The document must indicate that it is a "Capability Statement."

In some states, a capability statement is required to get your company certified as a minority business enterprise/women business enterprise. The capability statement can be provided to buyers and various government agencies. The next time you send an email to pitch your company, attach the capability statement, or you can include the capability statement link which is posted on your website.

Common sections in the Capability Statement:

- » Company overview/data

- » Core Competencies

- » Past Performance

- » Differentiators

- » Certifications

- » Pertinent Codes

- » Company contacts information

The capability statements in this book are from minority and women business owners. Please support their business by making a purchase.

Moore Business Success, LLC
CAPABILITES STATEMENT

Moore Business Success, LLC is a woman-owned boutique consulting firm that specializes in assisting small businesses, entrepreneurs, and start-up technology firms navigate through business compliance, contract formation, human resources benefits management and legal strategic planning. We are collaborative and team-oriented, driven to leave clients more informed, empowered, compliant, and successful than we found them. For Moore Assistance, contact us at info@moorebusinesssuccess.com

CORE COMPETENCIES

- Business Entity Formation and Dissolution
- Real Estate Purchase Agreements
- Governing Contract Creation
- Independent Contractor Agreements
- Human Resources Management
- Intellectual Property Security
- Employee Benefits Agreements
- Legal Strategic Planning
- Continuing Education Instructor
- Succession Planning

DIFFERENTIATORS

- Seasoned Professional
- Sr. Compliance Investigator
- Negotiated millions in RE
- Former litigator
- 20+ Years Adjunct Professor

CERTIFICATIONS

Juris Doctorate (1998)

L.LM Taxation (2006)

Retirement Benefits Associate Cert.

Group Benefits Advisor Cert.

MWBE- Certification (New Jersey)

NAIC CODES

91840 - EE Benefits Consulting Services

92400 - Educational/Training Services

91874 - Legal Consulting

92416 -Course Development Services

Your success is our business

Miller Resource Group

The Athletes Career Coach
Established 2018

My Notes

WIN # 3

PERSISTENCE

Procurement Queen Tip: You will remain persistent and continue to pitch your business to surpass 1million dollars in revenue. Winning government contracts will become part of your business model.

I_____ pledge on _____Month _____Day _____Year to remain persistent in my business to surpass a million dollars in revenue.

Signature: _____

My Notes

WIN #4

CREATE A VISION

Procurement Queen Tip: Proverbs 29:18 King James Version "Where there is no vision, the people perish: but he that keepeth the law, happy is he." Use the space below and the following page to cut out and paste images of the goals you want to achieve. Use magazines, write words of encouragement. It is a vision board in the book. Include words like Win, Contracts, Millions or Billions.

.

Paste images of the goals you want to achieve

Paste images of the goals you want to achieve

My Notes

WIN # 5

CHECKLIST

Procurement Queen Tip: Below is the winning list of tools for you to stay ready for opportunities. Check the box when you have the tools.

- ❏ Register your business.

- ❏ Federal Tax Identification Number (TIN or EIN)

- ❏ Register with System for Award Management (SAM)

- ❏ Get your Commercial and Government Entity (CAGE) Code

- ❏ Get your DUNS Number

- ❏ Register for email bid notifications to get alerts on current opportunities

- ❏ Register in supplier diversity vendor portals

- ❏ Attend procurement expo

- ❏ Attend procurement outreach events

- ❏ Open a business checking account

- ❏ Open a business saving account

- ❏ A copy of the business certificate of formation

- ❏ Get your business certified

- ❏ Create a capability statement

- ❏ Purchase your company domain name

- ❏ Create a company website

- ❏ Create your company name on various social media platforms (Instagram, Facebook, etc.)

- ❏ Attend government outreach events

- ❑ Attend pre-proposal meeting

- ❑ Attend bid walkthroughs

- ❑ Attend bid openings

- ❑ Respond to a various government solicitation

- ❑ Respond to a Request For Proposal (RFP)

- ❑ Respond to a Request For Qualification (RFQ)

- ❑ Respond to a Request For Information (RFI)

- ❑ Respond to a Request For Quotation (RFQ)

- ❑ Build relationships with government officials such as purchasing agents, buyers, procurement specialists, business unit stakeholders, etc

- ❑ Establish a LinkedIn profile

- ❑ Create a professional resume

- ❑ Create a company logo

- ❑ Trademark your brand

- ❑ Register your business to receive bid notifications from government agencies

- ❑ Create a professional email address for your business

- ❑ Join a procurement association

- ❑ Create a statement of work (SOW)

- ❑ Find at least five (5) mobile notaries in your area

- ❑ Get professional references from current and prior customers

- ❑ Get your business 8(a) Business Development program

- ❑ Create a business plan

- ❑ Join your local chamber of commerce

- ❑ Book a session to talk to Procurement Queen

- ❑ Purchase a service at www.procurementqueen.com

- ❑ Join Procurement Queen free Facebook groups

- ❑ Join Procurement Queen mailing list

- ❑ Create a mailing list for your business

- ❑ Donate/Give back to an organization

- ❑ Create a scholarship fund

- ❑ Write a book to showcase your expertise

- ❑ _____

- ❑ _____

- ❑ _____

- ❑ _____

- ❑ _____

- ❑ _____

- ❑ _____

- ❑ _____

- ❑ _____

- [ ] _____
- [ ] _____
- [ ] _____
- [ ] _____
- [ ] _____
- [ ] _____
- [ ] _____
- [ ] _____
- [ ] _____
- [ ] _____
- [ ] _____
- [ ] _____
- [ ] _____
- [ ] _____
- [ ] _____
- [ ] _____
- [ ] _____
- [ ] _____
- [ ] _____
- [ ] _____

- ☐ _____
- ☐ _____
- ☐ _____
- ☐ _____
- ☐ _____
- ☐ _____
- ☐ _____
- ☐ _____
- ☐ _____

My Notes

WIN # 6

GET LEGIT

Procurement Queen Tip: To be taken seriously as you compete for government contracts, you want your business to be legitimate. If you are selling a good or service that is legal, there are opportunities available for you to compete for government contracts or supplier diversity programs. I want you to get your business registered. It can be nonprofit or for-profit; it does not matter when it comes to competing for government contracts. Yes, the pastor can respond to and win a government-issued Request For Proposal (RFP) or bid. Also, some companies have a general business name and win government contracts for uniforms, beauty products, or dog food. Nonprofit companies win government contracts too.

Step 1: Decide which business entity you are going to form

BUSINESS ENTITY	ADVANTAGE/PROS	DISADVANTAGE/CONS
Sole Proprietorship		
Corporation		
Non-Profit		
Partnership		
S-Corporation		
Limited Liability Company (LLC)		
C-Corporation		

Action Required: The type of business entity that I want to start is: _____
_____

- ❑ Sole Proprietorship

- ❑ Partnership

- ❑ Corporation

- ❑ Limited Liability Company (LLC)

- ❑ Nonprofit

- ❑ S-Corporation

- ❑ C-Corporation

My Notes

WIN # 7

COMPANY OVERVIEW

Procurement Queen Tip: Complete the sections below; this information is needed for your capability statement and various procurement solicitations.

Company Data

Write the name of your business _____

_____

My business was registered in the state of _____

_____

My business was registered in the Month _____ Day _____ Year

_____.

Number of employees: _____

It cost $ _____ to register my business.

Write your company information

Address _____

_____

Telephone number _____

Mobile number _____

Fax number _____

Email address _____

Website _____

The Owner or Key personnel:

Name: _____

Title _____

Phone Number _____

Email: _____

Name: _____

Title _____

Phone Number _____

Email: _____

Name: _____

Title _____

Phone Number _____

Email: _____

Name: _____

Title _____

Phone Number _____

Email: _____

Name: _____

Title _____

Phone Number _____

Email: _____

Track the Revenue year over year:

Year _____ revenue $_____

Year _____ revenue $_____

Year _____ revenue $_____

Year _____ revenue $_____

Year _____ revenue $_____

Year _____ revenue $_____

Year _____ revenue $_____

Year _____ revenue $_____

Year _____ revenue $_____

Year _____ revenue $_____

Year _____ revenue $_____

Year _____ revenue $_____

Year _____ revenue $_____

Year _____ revenue $_____

Year _____ revenue $_____

Year _____ revenue $_____

Year _____ revenue $_____

My Notes

WIN # 8

BUSINESS DESCRIPTION

Write key words that describe my business

....

....

....

....

Write your business description in at least 3 sentences (include geographic areas you serve)

....

....

....

....

....

....

....

....

My Notes

WIN # 9

BUSINESS LICENSE

List the Industry licenses you have for your business, such as an electrical license. I want you to have a copy of the license in a secure place:

....

....

....

....

....

List of certifications you have for your business, such as food serving etc.:

....

....

....

....

....

....

My Notes

WIN # 10

NAICS CODE

Procurement Queen Tip: Search for North American Industry Classification System (NAICS) Codes that are related to the core competencies of your business. NAICS is the standard used to classify business establishments for the purpose of collecting, analyzing, and publishing statistical data related to the U.S. business economy. You can use the list of keywords for your business that you wrote in **WIN #8.**

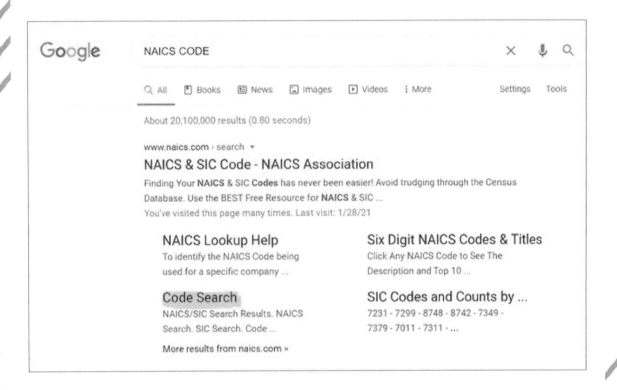

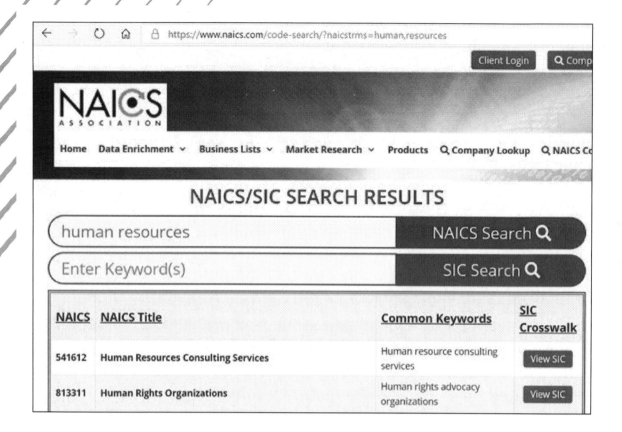

Fill-in your NAICS Code and NAICS Title

NAICS Code	NAICS Title
541612	Human Resources Consulting Services

NAICS Code	NAICS Title

My Notes

WIN # 11

GET A EIN

Procurement Queen Tip: An Employer Identification Number (EIN) is also known as a Federal Tax Identification Number and is used to identify a business entity. I recommend that you get an EIN when competing for government contracts. Keep in mind that the records you submit to the government can be provided to the public in accordance with the Freedom Of Information Act (FOIA). You may apply for an EIN for *free via the Internal Revenue Service immediately*.

My Employer Identification Number (EIN) Number is _____

Apply for the TIN: https://www.irs.gov/

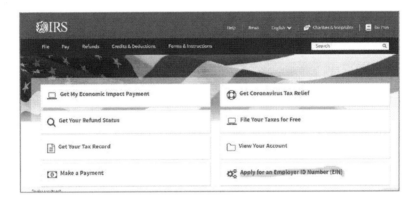

My Notes

WIN # 12

REGISTER WITH SAM

Procurement Queen Tip: Register your business to sell goods and services to the Federal government. System for Award Management (SAM) is the official U.S. Government system you need to register with to compete for opportunities with various federal agencies. It is FREE to register on SAM.gov for any entity. You will get your CAGE Code automatically when you apply to SAM.

1) Register: SAM.gov

2) Write your username _____

3) Password _____

4) My SAM number is _____

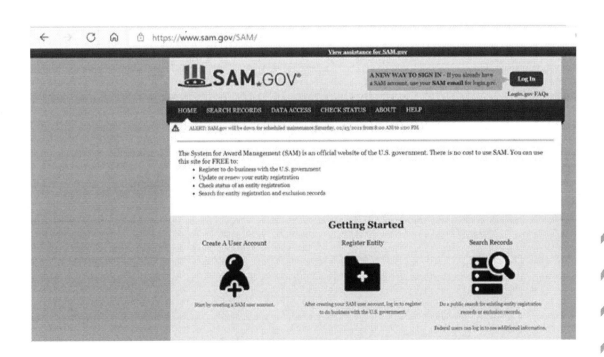

My Notes

WIN # 13

COMMERCIAL AND GOVERNMENT ENTITY (CAGE) CODE

Procurement Queen Tip: A CAGE Code is a five-character ID number used to identify your business and will be automatically assigned to you when you register with SAM. You do not need to have a CAGE code to create a capability statement, and you can include the CAGE code on your capability statement.

My Commercial and Government Entity (CAGE) Code is _____

My Notes

WIN # 14

DUN & BRADSTREET (D&B) NUMBER

Procurement Queen Tip: Navigate to Dun & Bradstreet (D&B) to create a DUNS Number, a unique nine-digit identification number, for each physical location of your business. DUNS Number assignment is FREE for all businesses and is required to register with the U.S. Federal Government for contracts or grants.

Apply for your DUNS Number: https://www.dnb.com/

My DUNS Number is _____.

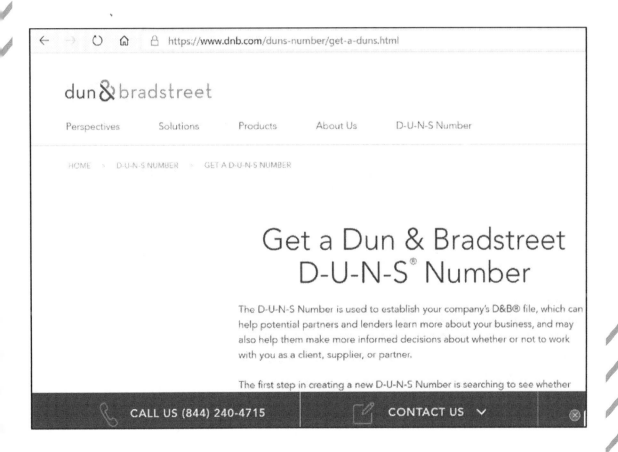

My Notes

WIN # 15

CORE COMPETENCIES

Procurement Queen Tip: A Capability Statement is a snapshot of your company and it should be one page, but if it is longer, make it front and back and no more than two keywords pages. It tells potential buyers and clients who you are and how you are different from your competitors. Your capability statement includes the core competencies of your business and should be listed as bullets.

What are your company's Core Competencies? Reflect on what it is that your company does best.

- ❏ _____
- ❏ _____
- ❏ _____
- ❏ _____
- ❏ _____
- ❏ _____
- ❏ _____
- ❏ _____
- ❏ _____
- ❏ _____
- ❏ _____

Examples of Core Competencies/Expertise:

- ❏ Change management, Leadership Training
- ❏ Process improvement, Project Management
- ❏ Web and Print Publications
- ❏ Content Strategy and Marketing Plan
- ❏ Wallpaper Removal
- ❏ Interior Painting, Best Pricing
- ❏ Global supply
- ❏ Customer service 24/7
- ❏ Minority media outreach
- ❏ Partnership development
- ❏ Website Management
- ❏ Social Media Management
- ❏ Brand Creation
- ❏ Logo Creation
- ❏ Contemporary Southern Cuisine with a creative twist
- ❏ Commercial Construction Cleanup

My Notes

WIN # 16

DIFFERENTIATORS

Procurement Queen Tip: The differentiator section in your Capability Statement should display unique techniques, awards, and recognitions. Why should the government and major companies award you a contract? Use this section to stand out from your competitors.

What are your company's differentiators?

❑ _____

❑ _____

❑ _____

❑ _____

❑ _____

❑ _____

❑ _____

❑ _____

❑ _____

❑ _____

❑ _____

Examples of differentiators:

- ❑ Certified PMP Involved in every project

- ❑ 20 years combined project and engineering experience

- ❑ Author of the Capability Statement Simple Guide

- ❑ Competitive pricing, prompt project completion

- ❑ We hire veterans

- ❑ Excellent Customer Service

- ❑ We make custom cups with maps for any location around the world

- ❑ We use ingredients free of toxins.

- ❑ 100% Owned Service Disabled Veteran (SDVOSB)

- ❑ Strong Cyber Security Expertise in Department of Defense and Commercial vulnerability research and development.

- ❑ Bilingual capabilities (English/Spanish)

- ❑ Accreditation in public relations

- ❑ Certified Professional in Supplier Diversity

- ❑ Centrally based in Northern New Jersey

My Notes

WIN # 17

PRODUCTS & SERVICES

Procurement Queen Tip: List 15 products and services you can sell to the government and private companies. If your product or service is legal, there are opportunities for your business. I recommended a yoga instructor for a contract award valued at $700,000.

State of Hawaii
Department of Public Safety
Corrections Program Services
Education Division

Request for Proposals

**RFP No. 20-CPS/E-16
Yoga Training for Male and Female
Inmates on Oahu**

March 3, 2020

REQUEST FOR QUOTES
Apparel Screen Printing &
Embroidery Service

CITY OF MOORHEAD
Holly Heitkamp, Moorhead Parks and Recreation Director
11/14/2019

Products	Services

My Notes

WIN # 18

GET CERTIFIED

Procurement Queen Tip: I highly recommend that you get your company certified if you qualify. The certification should be listed on your capability statement. Certifications provide your company with opportunities that only companies that are certified have access to. Some government agencies give you extra points during the evaluation of the RFP if you are certified, and there are set-aside opportunities that can only be awarded to vendors who are certified. There is a lot of money in budgets that have goals attributed to awarding companies that are certified.

Here is a loophole, your state and federal certification can be used to get access to major corporation's supplier diversity programs, and this is because your state did the vetting process to determine that you have met the requirements to get certified. You can include the certification logo on your capability statement.

A few Certification types:

- ❑ Minority-owned Business Enterprise (MBE): individuals within the following racial or ethnic groups: Black, Hispanic, Asian-Pacific, Asian-Indian, or Native American

- ❑ Women-owned Business Enterprise (WBE): women, regardless of race or ethnicity.

- ❑ Veteran Business Enterprise (VBE): individuals who have served in active duty in the United States military.

- ❑ Service-disabled Veteran-owned Business Enterprise (SDVBE): individuals who have served in active duty in the United States military and were disabled as a result of that service.

- ❑ People with Disabilities (PWD) – owned: individuals who have a disability regardless of how that disability occurred.

❑ Lesbian, Gay, Bisexual, or Transgender (LGBT) – owned: individuals that are lesbian, gay, bisexual, or transgendered.

❑ 8(a) Business Development program

My business in certified as a _____(Fill in based on the list above).

My business is certified in the state of _____

The name of the organization that certified my business is_____

My certification number is _____

My certification expires on _____

Certifications may provide preference to your business when pursuing business opportunities and government contracts, but keep in mind that this alone will not make your business qualified for a specific contract.

In this RFP, you will get 5 points if you are certified. Those 5 points could be the difference needed to win a $1m contract. Get certified in your state ASAP.

5. Exceptions/Alternatives.
   i.   Detail any exceptions taken to the *Scope of Work* and *Terms and Conditions* sections of this RFP. For each exception, specify the RFP page number, section number, and the exception taken. Offeror must not incorporate its standard contract document into its proposal, by reference or in full text, without listing each exception it represents to the terms and conditions of this RFP, as described in the *Exceptions/Alternatives* section of this RFP.
   ii. Detail any proposed alternatives the City's requirements as outlined in this RFP.
6. Minority/Woman Owned Programs. Provide details about your status as a minority or woman owned business.

I. **Proposal Scoring**. The following criteria and point scale will be used to evaluate the proposal:

Criteria	Maximum Points
Scope of Work • Ability to provide requested services	30 points
Past Project Experience & References • Proven Technical Competence in conducting analyses of courses & facilities • Proven Technical Competence in (re)design of golf courses	25 points
Capability and Skills - Credentials and Experience of Team	15 points
Project Schedule & Proposed Timeline	15 points
Project Fee Structure & Cost Estimate	10 points
Minority/Woman Owned Participation	5 points
Total	100 points

J. **Procedure for Evaluation of Proposals**
   1. After the proposal opening, the City will select for further consideration two or more Offerors deemed to be fully qualified and best suited among those submitting proposals based on Offerors' responses to the information requested in this RFP.

Procurement Queen Tip: Search for certification in your state.

Go to: www.google.com

Enter: "MBE Certification Arizona"   or Enter "WBE Certification Arizona"

Note: Change the state in your search criteria. "MBE Certification _____(enter your state)

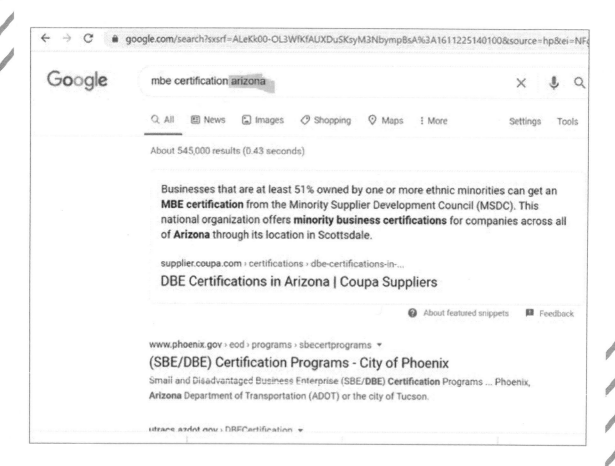

Procurement Queen Tip: Search for supplier diversity program at major corporations. Not all corporations have supplier diversity programs. When you find a company, register in their vendor portal and upload your capability statement if their portals allow you to upload attachments.

Go to: www.google.com

Enter: "Supplier Diversity Delta Airlines"

Note: Change the name of the company in your search criteria. "Supplier Diversity _____(enter the name of a corporation)

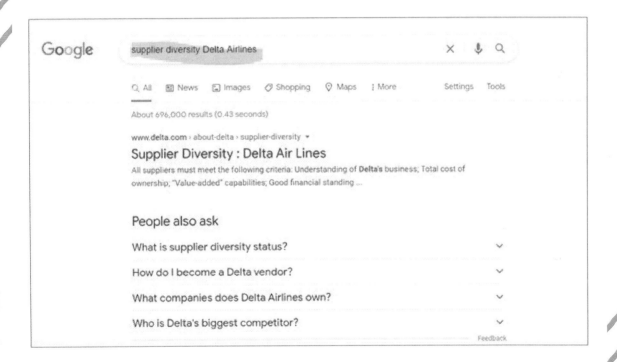

Supplier Diversity Vendor Registration

Company Name	Website	Username	Password

My Notes

WIN # 19

PRIOR PERFORMANCE

Procurement Queen Tip: Reviews matter. I recommend that you ask your clients for feedback during a project, especially after completing milestones. When competing for government contracts and supplier diversity opportunities, a written recommendation on your client's letterhead is preferred. Your capability statement should include the contact information of prior clients. It is okay to have several capability statements, specifically marketing to the agency's/ corporation needs. The capability statement is a living document, which means you should update it periodically.

Action Required: Use the steps below to provide proof of prior experience.

Client Name: _____

Company Name: _____

Company Address: _____

Phone Number: _____

Email address:_____

Project description: _____

Project amount: _____

Client Name: _____

Company Name: _____

Company Address: _____

Phone Number: _____

Email address:_____

Project description: _____

Project amount: _____

Client Name: _____

Company Name: _____

Company Address: _____

Phone Number: _____

Email address:_____ . _____

Project description: _____

Project amount: _____

Client Name: _____

Company Name: _____

Company Address: _____

Phone Number: _____

Email address:_____

Project description: _____

Project amount: _____

Client Name: _____

Company Name: _____

Company Address: _____

Phone Number: _____

Email address:_____

Project description: _____

Project amount: _____

My Notes

WIN # 20

CREATE THE CAPABILITY STATEMENT

Procurement Queen Tip: You are ready to create the capability statement, and you have all the components. You can use Microsoft Word or Canva to create some visually appealing capability statement.

Link: https://www.canva.com/

Under the Documents, there are Resume templates you can use to create the capability statement, or you can create or modify existing templates. In the template add the section for core competencies, company data, past performance, etc.

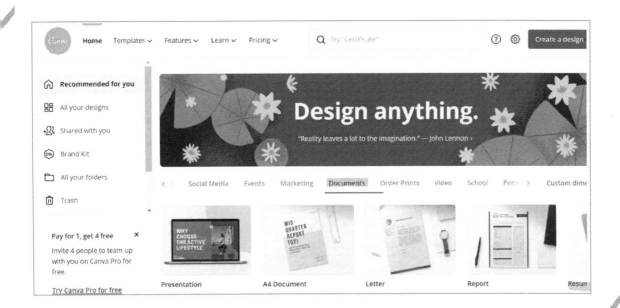

My Notes

WIN # 21

OPEN A BUSINESS BANKING ACCOUNT

Procurement Queen Tip: Research banks or credit unions in your area to open a business banking account. Along with the benefits, compare the fees, the minimum deposit required, and interest rate. Keep the document that states that you are the authorized signer on the bank account; some states require this language from the bank to get your company certified. See the example of the bank letter.

Bank/Credit Union Name	Bank/Credit Union Website	Minimum deposit and interest rate	Fees

I opened the business banking account at _____ (fill in the name of the bank).

The business banking account was opened on _____Month _____Day _____Year.

The contact information for my personal banker is:

Fist Name _____ Last Name _____

Phone number _____

Email address_____

Bank location Address _____City _____

State _____Zip code_____

P
ROCUREMENT QUEEN ™ Bank

"Bank on this queen"

February 14, 2021

Sterlyn Law Firm, LLC
60980 Park Place
Hill, NJ 07071

To Whom It May Concern:

This letter is a verification that the customer named above Sterlyn Law Firm, LLC has an active checking account with Procurement Queen Bank. Sterlyn Williams is an authorized signer for the account Sterlyn Law Firm, LLC.

Account Number	Date Opened
18713426809	2/8/21

If you have any questions, please contact me at: 908-313-9087
A representative will be happy to assist you as follows:

Monday – Friday 9:00 – 5:00PM Eastern

Thank You. We appreciate your business.

Sincerely,

Phoenix Williams

Phoenix Williams
Personal Banker
Procurement Queen Bank

Sterlyn Williams

Sterlyn Williams
Chief Executive Officer
Sterlyn Law Firm, LLC

My Notes

WIN # 22

LEARN THE TERMINOLOGY

Procurement Queen Tip: I want you to learn the terminology because it will help increase your confidence as you embark on your procurement journey. You will use the terminology to ask questions like a pro. I told you I want to see you win.

Term	Definition	Example of the term	Use the Term
Requisition	A request to purchase a good or service.	Sterlyn is the Director of Student Engagement at Convent High School. Sterlyn created a **requisition** for Phoenix Antibullying LLC to teach the kids at Convent High School about bullying and gang violence. The requisition number is 00129876	Good morning Ms. Sterlyn. My name is Phoenix Williams; we met a few weeks ago regarding teaching the students about bullying and gang violence. Can you please let me know if the **requisition** was entered and if so, please provide me with the requisition number? **Procurement Queen Tip:** Eventually, when the requisition is fully approved, a purchase order number is generated. The purchase order is your contract. Always have a purchase order before you provide a good or service.

Procurement	Procurement is the sourcing of activities, negotiation, and strategic selection of goods and services that are important to an organization ("buy stuff"). Procurement refers to the processes used by the Division to establish formal contracts by which using agencies can purchase required goods and services.	The government and major corporations buy janitorial services, furniture, or water by issuing a bid, Request For Quotations (RFQ), Request For Proposal (RFP), Request For Information (RFI), or Request For Qualification (RFQ)	Can you please let me know if this governmental entity procures/sources janitorial services?
Purchase Order	A purchaser's written document to a supplier formalizing all the terms and conditions of a proposed transaction, such as the description of the requested items, cost of items being purchased, delivery schedule, terms of payment, and transportation.	When the requisition was approved, I received a copy of the purchase order.	The purchase order number is always entered on the invoices I submit to accounts payable for payment. I always make sure the price/unit cost on the purchase order and on my invoice reconcile.
Accounts Payable	An accounting function that is responsible for making payments to contractors according to the contract terms and conditions.	The accounts payable department issued me a check after I submitted my invoice and the requesting department entered a receipt acknowledging they received my goods/ service.	If I do not receive a payment within 30 days, I always reach out to the account payable department to check the status.

Buyer	A purchaser or procurer of products and services. This title may also refer to an individual who is responsible for the procurement activities of an entity, also commonly referred to as a purchasing or procurement agent.	I emailed the buyer for marketing services a copy of my capability statement, which included the key differentiator for marketing campaigns.	I emailed the buyer to find out if a marketing Request For Proposal (RFP) will be issued this year.
Supplier	A person or business that provides goods and/or services.	I am a supplier because I sell my products/ services to the government.	My capability statement includes my company overview and NAICS, so the buyer or business unit liaisons learn about the goods/services I provide.
FOIA	Since 1967, the Freedom of Information Act (FOIA) has provided the public the right to request access to records from any federal agency. It is often described as the law that keeps citizens in the know about their government. Federal agencies are required to disclose any information requested under the FOIA unless it falls under one of nine exemptions that protect interests such as personal privacy, national security, and law enforcement.	The supplier completed a FOIA request to get a copy of the winning Auditing proposals of the prior bids. The supplier wants to see what the contract award is and all the supporting documents.	I completed the FOIA form to receive a copy of RFP #2353 auditing in the contract that was issued in February 2021. I received a redacted copy after 7 days from my request. Now I have a better understanding of how to respond to this type of RFP.

My Notes

WIN # 23

BID NOTIFICATIONS

Procurement Queen Tip: I want you to register on various government agencies' vendor/supplier registration portal so that you can receive bid notifications automatically in your email. The government vendor portal is often free, so be sure to do your diligence, especially if you have to enter your credit card number, most legitimate government website end with "gov." I recommend that you create a free email account to use when you register for bid notifications to avoid filling up your primary business inbox with bidding opportunities. Most of the information required to register you wrote down is the prior WINs. I want you to stay ready.

❑ Full Name

❑ Company Name

❑ Categories for your business

❑ Business Address

❑ Tax Identification Number

❑ Email address

❑ Phone Number

❑ Date of business formation (mmddyyyy)

❑ Completed W-9 form

Find a vendor registration portal by searching on Google. You can customize the Google search to include your state, city, town, etc.

Some search examples are:

Vendor registration portal in NJ

Vendor registration portal in Essex County, NJ

Supplier registration portal in Essex County, NJ

Supplier registration for colleges

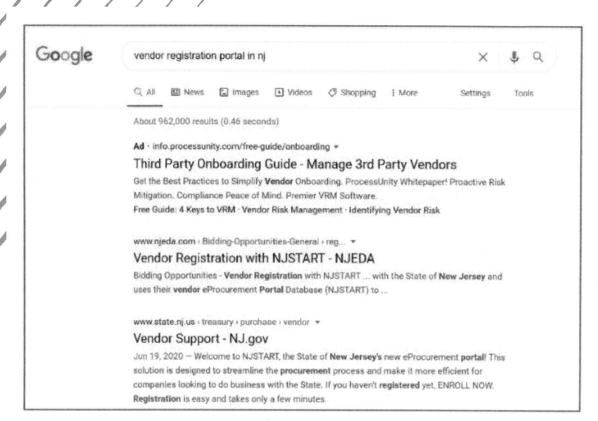

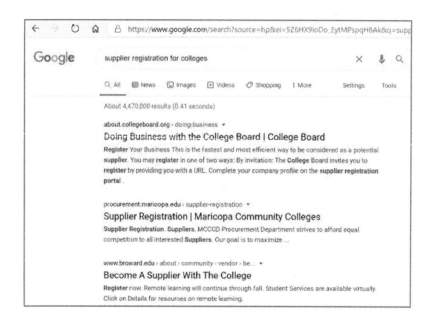

An example of a vendor portal is shown below

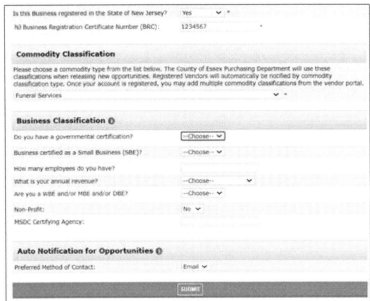

List the vendor portals you found. You will register to those portals so that you will receive the bid notifications related to your business.

Government Agency Name	Vendor Portal/Link	Username	Passwords

My Notes

WIN #24

BUILD RELATIONSHIPS

Procurement Queen Tip: I want you to start to build a relationship with the buyers and department heads or business units at government agencies or private organizations. Focus on the buyers that source (buy) the goods or services you provide. Find the buyer's contact information, so you email them your capability statement and update them on new goods/services. Your good/service must align with their mission to add value. There so many agencies, so I recommend that you narrow your search to companies that you want to work with.

Buyer Job Titles: Look for these titles when you search on LinkedIn or at agency websites

- Buyer

- Contract Specialist

- Sourcing Analyst

- Lead Buyer

- Senior Buyer

- Purchasing Agent

- Purchasing Specialist

- Procurement Officer

- Contract Officer

- Sourcing Specialist

- Chief Procurement Officer

- Procurement Analyst

- Procurement Associate

A few ways to quickly find a buyer:

1. Look for the purchasing directory on the agency's website. Write down the buyer's contact information. It is important that you do your due diligence and register on the agency vendor portal if they have one, then email the buyer a copy of your capability statement.

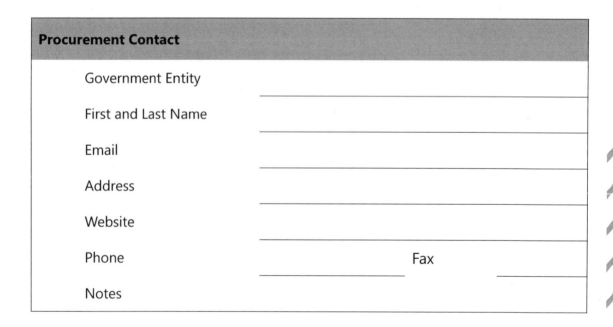

Procurement Contact

Government Entity

First and Last Name

Email

Address

Website

Phone   Fax

Notes

Procurement Contact

Government Entity

First and Last Name

Email

Address

Website

Phone   Fax

Notes

Procurement Contact

Government Entity

First and Last Name

Email

Address

Website

Phone   Fax

Notes

Procurement Contact

Government Entity

First and Last Name

Email

Address

Website

Phone   Fax

Notes

2. Another method you can use to find a buyer is to look for current and past bidding opportunities to see if the buyer's contact information is part of the Request For Proposal (RFP)/Bid/Quote.

JACKSON COUNTY
REQUEST FOR PROPOSALS
CLEANING SERVICES FOR COUNTY FACILITIES
RFP 2021-09

The Jackson County Board of County Commissioners is seeking a qualified company/firm to perform professional cleaning and janitorial services for several County facilities. The cleaning and janitorial services to be performed would be on a weekly basis for approximately 20 different County facilities. It is the intent of the County to select and negotiate one contract, to be renewed annually, with a firm that meets the requirements outlined in the RFP.

*Submittals must include the following:
1. Submittal Cover Sheet
2. Firm qualifications and capabilities
3. Qualifications, resumes, certifications, and licenses of proposed professional personnel
4. Client references for similar projects
5. Experience on similar projects
6. Evidence of registration and statement of professional liability insurance and license(s)

Procurement Contact

Government Entity

First and Last Name

Email

Address

Website

Phone   Fax

Notes

Procurement Contact

Government Entity

First and Last Name

Email

Address

Website

Phone   Fax

Notes

3. Another method you can use to find a buyer is to use Google.

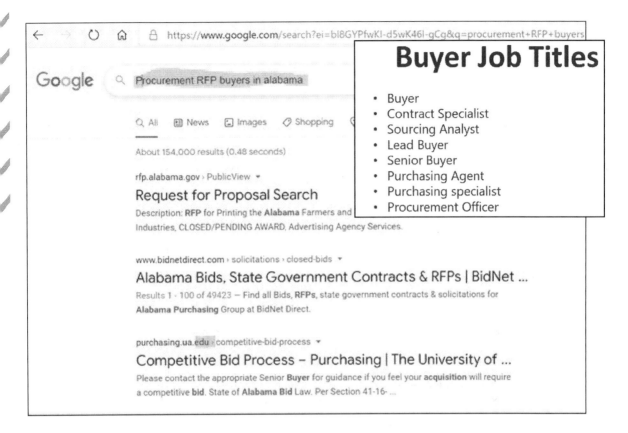

Procurement Contact

Government Entity

First and Last Name

Email

Address

Website

Phone   Fax

Notes

Procurement Contact

Government Entity

First and Last Name

Email

Address

Website

Phone   Fax

Notes

4. Another method you can use to find a buyer is to use the search option in LinkedIn and search for the buyer title followed by the company/agency name.

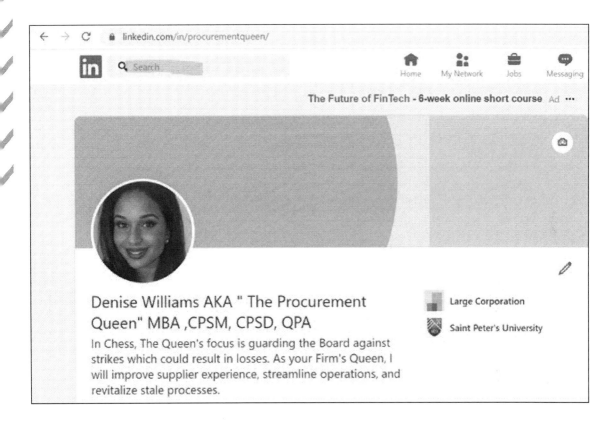

Amirah Lawson the owner of Unicorn Consulting, LLC re-vamped my LinkedIn profile + Resume. Amirah did a great job and I am a happy client, plus she is a minority owned business. You need a professional resume when you compete for government contracts, such as Request For Proposal, Request For Qualifications. Hire Amirah today Unicornconsultingllc@gmail.com

Procurement Contact

Government Entity

First and Last Name

Email

Address

Website

Phone   Fax

Notes

Procurement Contact

Government Entity

First and Last Name

Email

Address

Website

Phone   Fax

Notes

My Notes

WIN # 25

FIND CONTRACTOR/PRIME CONTRACTORS

Procurement Queen Tip: In addition to building relationships with buyers at government agencies, I also want you to build a relationship with other companies, especially companies who are competing for contracts and are certified as a minority/women/veteran business. Several agencies have a database where you can search for vendors in your state; you can email a copy of your capability statement to them and start to build a relationship.

New Jersey Selective Assistance Vendor Information (NJSAVI) allows you to search for vendors that you can partner with and includes the contact information making it easy for you to start to build that relationship. Keep in mind that you can compete for contracts in various states, so if you are a Florida company, you can still partner with New Jersey companies.

Search your state for a similar database.

NJSAVI: **https://www20.state.nj.us/TYTR_SAVI/vendorSearch.jsp**

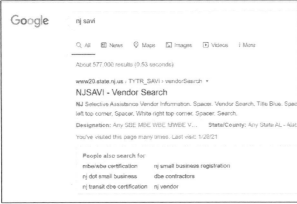

Contractors to contact

Company Name	First and last name	Telephone	Email

Procurement Queen Tip: Another method to find companies to partner with is to look for the pre-proposal sign-in sheet on the agency's website; you can also reach out to government agencies directly to request a copy of the sign-in sheet, sometimes referred to a plan holders log if it is not on the website. Please keep in mind that every solicitation (RFP/Quote/bid) does not have to include a pre-proposal meeting. The sign-in sheet includes the company name, email address, the name of the person that was present at the meeting, and the solicitation information. You can provide a copy of your capability statement to the companies listed.

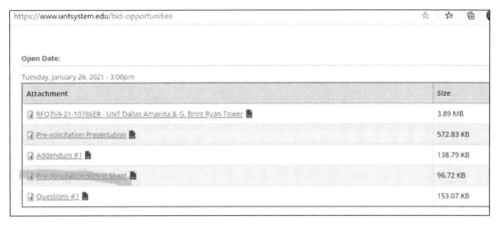

Look for the sign-in sheet on the government agency's website. Save the list to a folder or print it out.

Contractors to contact

Company Name	First and last name	Telephone	Email

My Notes

WIN # 26

PRE-PROPOSAL MEETING

Procurement Queen Tip: When a solicitation (RFP, bid, quote) is advertised, it may include a pre-proposal meeting invitation. The purpose of the pre-proposal (pre-bid) meeting is to answer questions from potential vendors and to clear any ambiguities. The government agencies recommend that potential vendors read the solicitation ahead of time so that a meaningful exchange can take place. These meetings are open and free to the public, so anyone can attend. Some pre-proposal meetings are mandatory, so if you intend to respond to the solicitation, you must attend. In some states, advertising a mandatory pre-proposal meeting is deemed to be too restrictive and is prohibited.

The government agencies' key personals relate to the solicitation present at the pre-proposal meeting, such as the buyers, end-users, various procurement officials, along with potential vendors. I recommend that when you attend, you distribute copies of your capability statement to everyone in attendance. We are currently in a pandemic fighting COVID-19, so most of these meetings are done virtually. Try to attend even though it is not related to the goods or services you provide. I want you to get the experience so you can listen to questions that are asked and you too can ask questions to improve your public speaking.

Find and Register for Pre-Proposal meeting

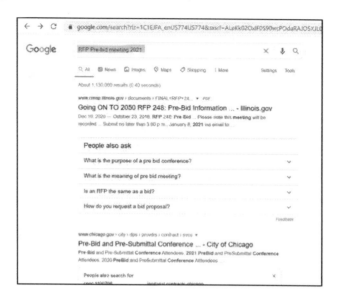

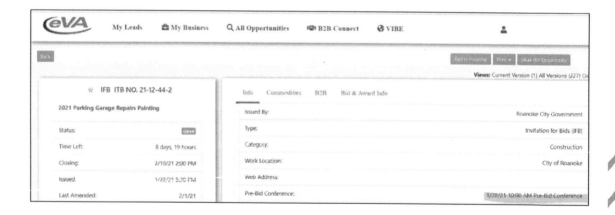

Find and Register for Pre-Proposal meeting

Pre-Proposal Meeting Date	Registration Information	Description of solicitation	Optional/Mandatory

My Notes

WIN # 27

EVENTS

Procurement Queen Tip: I want you to look for procurement events in your state, and then eventually, you will expand to attending events out of state. Procurement matchmaking events are a great way to connect with government agencies and private corporations' buyers. I recommend you bring a copy of the capability statement to distribute. You may find these events and procurement fairs listed on the agency's website, chamber of commerce, and various procurement associations. Also, follow these agencies on social media and signup for their mailing list.

List Events you are going to attend

Event Date	Event Time	Event Description	Event Location (in-person/ virtual)	Event Cost

My Notes

WIN # 28

TIME TO SELL

Procurement Queen Tips: Now that you have listed what you are going to sell, it is time to find the governmental entities and corporations that buy your product and service. The goal is to pitch your goods and services to them. I recommend that you look for opportunities in your state, and then you expand to other states. I am going to use New Jersey as an example, but you can do this for your state.

New Jersey snapshot:

- 21 counties and 566 municipalities.
- 1,866 public elementary schools.
- 398 public secondary schools.
- 132 private high schools.
- 20 four-year colleges.
- 21 two-year community colleges.

These government entities all purchase goods/services. Your job is to find out which one buys the products/ services you sell.

Write the name of your state:_____

List the four-year colleges in your state: _____

_____

_____

_____

List the two-year colleges _____

_____

_____

_____

_____

List the cities in your state: _____

_____

_____

_____

List the public board of education in your town:_____

_____

_____

My Notes

WIN # 29

PROCUREMENT HOUR

Procurement Queen Tip: I want you to create your Procurement Hour. The Procurement Hour is where you allocate one (1) hour during the week for procurement-related activities. Start to build relationships directly with a government agency, the prime contractor of major organizations. It is best to learn what agencies, organizations, or prime contractors need, and then demonstrate in your capability statement how your business can fulfill that need. On major holidays and/or special occasions, it is a good time to build relationships with buyers, procurement officials, contracting officers, etc. Send a happy birthday email, Happy New Year email, International Women's Day, Thanksgiving Day, send the email with the capability statement attached. A sample of the letter is below; you can customize the letter based on your company.

Idea: You can even create a custom company greeting card with your capability statement on the front cover or inside the card. Also, you can create a custom folded business card, and when you open it, a copy of the capability statement is in the interior.

Sample email message

Hi Procurement Team (if you do not know the name of the person),

Happy New Year!! I hope you are well and safe. Firstly, thank you for all your efforts during this pandemic crisis. My name is _____and I'm the owner of _____. We supply training to executives for compliance and workplace etiquette. I wanted to reach out and see if you have any needs for your city/county, etc. Would you be able to point me in the right direction of who might handle this?

Below is a short list of our training topics: I can send over a sample course outline for your review.

Hiring Best Practices

- How to have meaningful performance reviews

- How to create succession planning

Insert link to course if applicable:_____

The capability statement is attached. Let me know if you are interested and/or in need. I am here to help!

Stay Safe,

Denise Williams, Owner
Procurement Queen Corporation
New Jersey Certified Minority/Women Business Enterprise
(908) 313-9087
team@Procurementqueen.com
www.procurementqueen.com

Procurement Hour Task:

- ❑ Register for bid notifications (colleges, universities, government agencies, schools)

- ❑ Become familiar with the agency you are targeting; visit their website

- ❑ Follow the agency on social media.

- ❑ Follow-up at least monthly with new products, services, or well wishes

- ❑ Find out if the agency has a website with opportunities listed

- ❑ Attend outreach events, expos, training, and workshops

- ❑ Attend pre-proposal meetings

- ❑ Distribute your capability statement

- ❑ Connect with buyers on LinkedIn

- ❑ Read the agency annual report or major corporations investor reports

- ❑ Update your capability statement

Procurement Hour

Week # _____   Dates: _____

TASK	MONDAY	TUESDAY	WEDNESDAY	THURSDAY	FRIDAY
Register for Bid Notifications					
Find a Government buyer					
Follow-up					
Networking					

My Notes

WIN # 30

A WINNING ATTITUDE

Procurement Queen Tip: Mindset is important as you embark on this procurement journey. Feed your mind and body daily. Self-care is ongoing.

A few ideas

- ❑ Read the affirmation daily
- ❑ Create a vision board
- ❑ Meditate daily for at least 15 minutes and reflect
- ❑ Exercise for at least 30 minutes
- ❑ Read for 15 minutes
- ❑ Check your email
- ❑ Listen to a podcast
- ❑ Learn a new app that you can use for your business
- ❑ Learn a new skill
- ❑ Organize a closet
- ❑ Go hiking
- ❑ Join a professional group
- ❑ Volunteer at your favorite charity
- ❑ Take a relaxing bath
- ❑ Book a hotel room for yourself
- ❑ Hire a therapist
- ❑ Get a physical at the doctor

- ☐ _____
- ☐ _____
- ☐ _____
- ☐ _____
- ☐ _____
- ☐ _____
- ☐ _____
- ☐ _____

My Notes

WIN #31

GRATITUDE

Procurement Queen Tip: I want you to take a least 5 minutes to write down and say it out loud what you are grateful for. For example, I have two adorable little kids, and I am grateful for my eyesight because I get to see their smiles.

I am grateful for _____.

I am grateful for _____.

I am grateful for _____.

I am grateful for _____.

I am grateful for _____.

I am grateful for _____.

I am grateful for _____.

I am grateful for _____.

I am grateful for _____.

I am grateful for _____.

I am grateful for _____.

I am grateful for _____.

I am grateful for _____.

I am grateful for _____.

I am grateful for _____.

I am grateful for _____.

I am grateful for _____.

I am grateful for _____.

I am grateful for _____.

I am grateful for _____.

I am grateful for _____.

My Notes

WIN #32

CERTIFICATE

Procurement Queen Academy

CERTIFICATE OF COMPLETION

This is hereby granted to

for successfully completed all course requirements for the
Capability Statement in _____(year)

Denise Williams
_____

DENISE WILLIAMS, CEO
Procurement Queen
www.ProcurementQueen.com

Made in the USA
Columbia, SC
26 December 2022

74935237R00115